GRADE 6

WORCESTERSHIRE COUNTY COUNCIL CULTURAL SERVICES

The Syllabus of Examinations should be read for details of requirements, especially those for scales, aural tests and sight-reading. Attention should be paid to the Special Notices on the inside front cover, where warning is given of any changes.

The syllabus is obtainable from music retailers or from The Associated Board of the Royal Schools of Music, 14 Bedford Square, London WC1B 3JG (please send a stamped addressed C5 (162mm x 229mm) envelope).

In examination centres outside the UK, information and syllabuses may be obtained from the Local Representative.

CONTENTS

Where appropriate, pieces in this volume have been checked with original source material and edited as necessary for instructional purposes. Fingering, phrasing, pedalling, metronome marks and the editorial realization of ornaments (where given) are for guidance but are not comprehensive or obligatory.

Editor for the Associated Board: **Richard Jones**

DO NOT PHOTOCOPY © MUSIC

Alternative pieces for this grade

Music origination by Barnes Music Engraving Ltd.
Cover by Økvik Design.
Printed in England by Headley Brothers Ltd,
The Invicta Press, Ashford, Kent.

A:1

Jigg

Fourth movement from Suite No. 3 in B flat

CHILCOT

Thomas Chilcot (*c.*1700–66) was organist of Bath Abbey for nearly 40 years, from 1728 until his death. Dotted crotchets in the L.H. could be lightly detached, but melodic ones in the R.H. (bar 1 etc.) might be sustained. Dynamics are left to the player's discretion.
Source: *Six Suites of Lessons for the Harpsichord or Spinet* (London, n.d.).

Selected from Chilcot: *Three Keyboard Suites*, edited by Richard Jones (Associated Board)

Allegretto

Third movement from Sonata in B flat, K. 570

Edited by
Stanley Sadie & Denis Matthews

MOZART

The Sonata in B flat, K. 570, is a late work, composed in Vienna in February 1789. The main theme of the Allegretto (bars 1–22) is followed by two distinct episodes (starting at bars 23 and 45), of which the second is in the subdominant E flat. Finally, all three themes are brought together in the coda (bars 63ff.). Mozart provided dynamics only in the last eight bars: elsewhere they are left to the player's discretion.

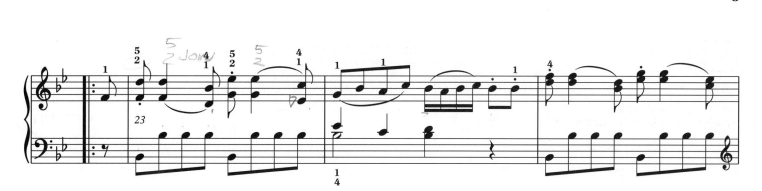

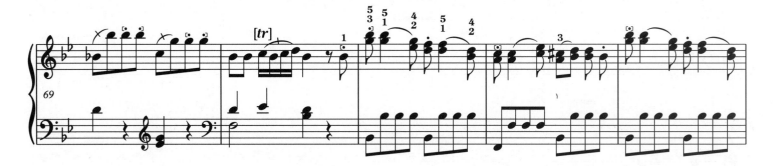

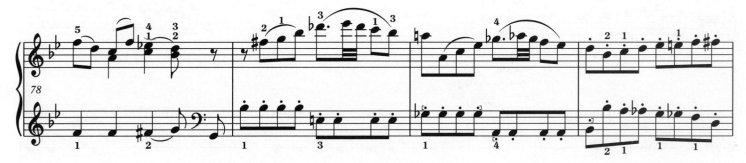

Fugue in E minor

TWV 30:25/1

No. 5 from *Fugues légères et petits jeux*

TELEMANN

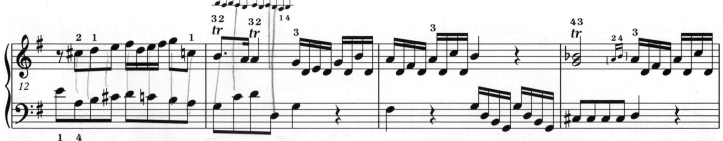

This is a two-part 'counter-fugue', i.e. a fugue whose subject is answered by its melodic inversion. Telemann uses this antiquated technique alongside episodes in a light, playful, even fashionable style (e.g. bars 13b–17). Crotchets might be lightly detached throughout, and the pair that opens the subject somewhat marked. A pause might be made on the chord that precedes the rest in bars 17 and 40. Dynamics are left to the player's discretion.

Source: *Fugues légères et petits jeux* (Hamburg, 1737).

Cloche des Matines

Op. 109 No. 9

Edited by
Alan Jones

J. F. BURGMÜLLER

Johann Friedrich Burgmüller (1806–74) settled in Paris, where he became a popular pianist, improvising hundreds of salon pieces and composing many works for the amateur player.

B:2

Vals poético No. 6

Edited by
Lionel Salter

GRANADOS

This is the sixth of seven romantic waltzes selected for publication in 1887 from the many written by the Spanish composer and pianist Enrique Granados (1867–1916) while he was still a student at the Madrid Conservatoire.

Reproduced from *Short Romantic Pieces for Piano*, Book 4, edited by Lionel Salter (Associated Board)

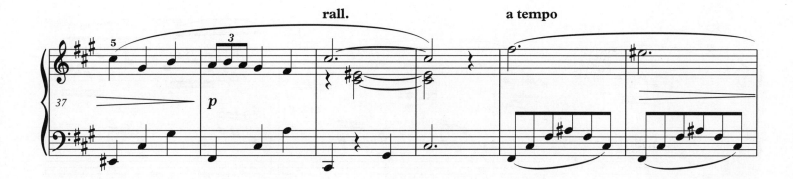

Song without Words

B:3

MENDELSSOHN

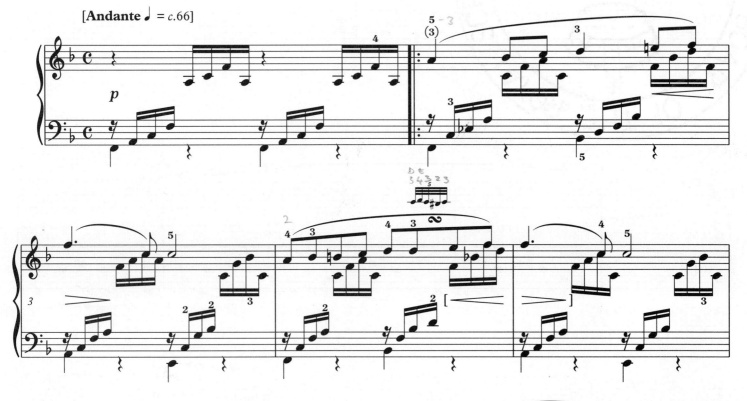

Around 1841 Mendelssohn entered this *Lied ohne Worte* in the music album of Fräulein Doris Loewe, daughter of Ferdinand Loewe who was an actor in the Viennese Court Theatre.

Source: facsimile of the autograph, *Die Musik*, Vol. 16 No. 11 (1923).

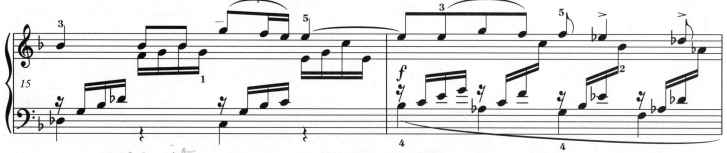

C:1

Rondo–Finale

No. 8 from *Reihe kleine Klavierstücke*

BADINGS

The prolific Dutch composer Henk Badings (1907–87) began his career as a mining engineer, but studied music with his compatriot Willem Pijper and in 1935 abandoned engineering entirely in favour of music.

ritenuto   a tempo

Modulations

from *Blue Piano*

MIKE CORNICK

C:2

The composer tells us that this and its companion pieces in the collection *Blue Piano* 'explore some of the melodic figures, rhythms and harmonies of jazz and blues in the context of the medium- and slow-tempo ballad'. All quavers should be swung, so that, for example, the first figure should be played:

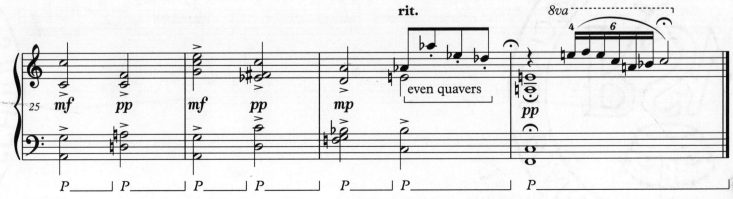

C:3

Legend

No. 6 from *Pictures of Childhood*

KHACHATURIAN

Lento ♩ = 69

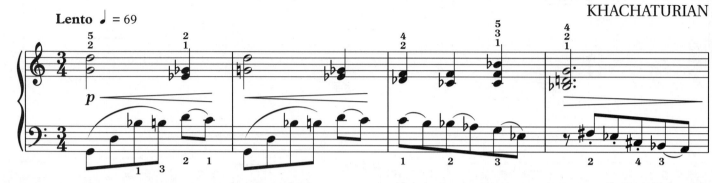

poco più mosso

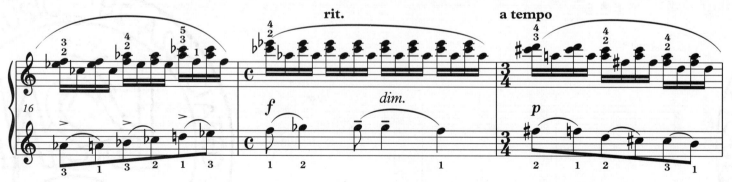

The Georgian composer Aram Il'yich Khachaturian (1903–78) wrote in a colourful, pictorial style incorporating folk idioms from Armenia and other southern republics of the former Soviet Union.

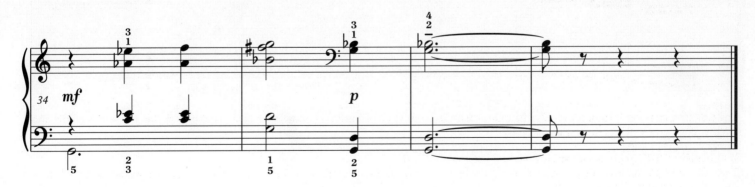